DON'T GIVE UP, CHARLIE BROWN

by Charles M. Schulz

Selected Cartoons from
You've Had It, Charlie Brown, Vol. 2

A FAWCETT CREST BOOK

Fawcett Publications, Inc., Greenwich, Connecticut

DON'T GIVE UP, CHARLIE BROWN

C'MON, GET A HIT! WE NEED A HIT! OOOO, HOW WE NEED A HIT! PLEASE, GET A HIT... PLEASE... PLEASE...

STRIKE ONE!

STRIKE TWO!

STRIKE THREE!

YOU DIDN'T EVEN SWING!
THAT'S GONNA COST YOU
HALF YOUR SUPPER TONIGHT!

SNIF!

RATS!
WHY CAN'T
I BE ROUGH,
AND TOUGH
AND MEAN LIKE
ALL THE OTHER
MANAGERS?

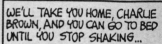

WHEN I'M REAL LONESOME, I LIKE TO GO TO MY DAD'S BARBER SHOP..

HE ALWAYS SMILES WHEN I GO IN, AND SAYS, "HI"

THE TWO MEN WHO WORK WITH HIM ARE NICE TO ME, TOO..

THEY ALWAYS ASK ME IF I'VE COME IN FOR A SHAVE..

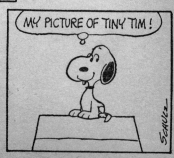

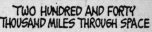

BEFORE I TAKE OFF, MY FAITHFUL GROUND CREW GATHERS ABOUT ME BIDDING FAREWELL.. THEY ARE VERY DISTURBED.. SOME FEEL THAT PERHAPS WE SHALL NEVER SEE EACH OTHER AGAIN...

WHAT AN EMOTIONAL MOMENT! THROATS TIGHTEN, AND TEARS WELL IN OUR EYES...

IS IT POSSIBLE THAT THIS COULD BE MY FINAL MISSION? THAT I SHALL NEVER RETURN? THAT THIS IS THE END?

FORGET IT!

SCHULZ

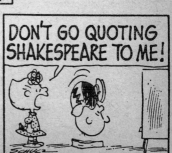

YES, MA'AM, I KNOW THERE ARE SEATS IN THE FRONT ROW... I WAS MERELY OBEYING THE BIBLICAL ADMONITION...

IN THE FOURTEENTH CHAPTER OF LUKE, BEGINNING WITH THE TENTH VERSE, WE READ, "...WHEN YOU ARE INVITED, GO AND SIT IN THE LOWEST PLACE SO THAT WHEN YOUR HOST COMES HE MAY SAY TO YOU, 'FRIEND, GO UP HIGHER';"

"...EVERY ONE WHO EXALTS HIMSELF WILL BE HUMBLED, AND HE WHO HUMBLES HIMSELF WILL BE EXALTED."

YES, MA'AM..

MISS OTHMAR ISN'T MUCH FOR BIBLICAL ADMONITIONS...

I'M GOING OVER TO THE PENCIL SHARPENER..THIS LEAD BROKE...

ACTUALLY, IT ISN'T LEAD AT ALL.. IT'S A COMBINATION OF BAVARIAN CLAY AND MADAGASCAR GRAPHITE

YOU'RE THE ONLY PERSON I KNOW WHO CAN TAKE THE JOY OUT OF SHARPENING A PENCIL !

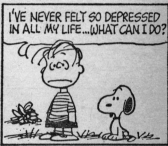

→

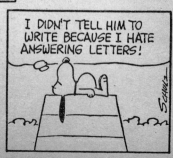

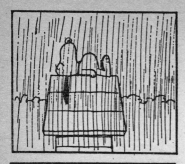

THIS IS THE SORT OF DREARY FALL RAIN THAT MAKES YOU WANT TO SIT INSIDE ALL DAY, AND STARE OUT THE WINDOW, AND DRINK TEA AND PLAY SAD SONGS ON THE STEREO

SO WHY AM I LYING HERE?

ANYONE WHO WOULD SIT AROUND BY HIMSELF MAKING FUNNY FACES MUST BE CRAZY

WHAT ELSE IS THERE TO DO ON A SATURDAY AFTERNOON WHEN YOUR GIRL FRIEND HAS LEFT YOU, YOUR TV SET IS BROKEN AND YOUR JOGGING SUIT IS IN THE WASH?

TOMORROW IS HALLOWEEN, SNOOPY..

TOMORROW NIGHT I'LL BE SITTING HERE IN THIS SINCERE PUMPKIN PATCH, AND I'LL SEE THE 'GREAT PUMPKIN'! HE'LL COME FLYING THROUGH THE AIR, AND I'LL BE HERE TO SEE HIM!

ISN'T THAT EXCITING?

WHEE!

I'M DRAWING A ROW OF TREES, AND I'M GOING TO COLOR THEM GREEN

THAT'S NOT ART

I'LL PUT A LAKE IN FRONT OF THE TREES

THAT STILL WON'T MAKE IT ART

AND BY THE LAKE I'LL DRAW A TINY LOG CABIN

AH, HA!!

CAUGHT YOU IN THE ACT, DIDN'T I?

TOMORROW IS BEETHOVEN'S BIRTHDAY..

I HAVE AN IDEA FOR A GREAT PARTY!

WE'LL INVITE AN EQUAL NUMBER OF BOYS AND GIRLS, SEE, AND EACH BOY WILL BRING A GIRL A NICE PRESENT...

AT THE APPOINTED TIME, EACH GIRL WILL OPEN HER PRESENT, AND THEN EACH GIRL WILL GIVE EACH BOY A WARM HUG AND A KISS!

TOMORROW IS BEETHOVEN'S BIRTHDAY..

I SHALL CELEBRATE HIS BIRTHDAY BY PLAYING HIS SONATA IN A FLAT MAJOR, OPUS 110, AND SITTING IN SILENT MEDITATION FOR ONE MINUTE... BY MYSELF!

TOMORROW IS MONDAY..

PEGGY FLEMING AND I USED TO SKATE TOGETHER QUITE OFTEN...

...BEFORE I BECAME BIG-TIME!

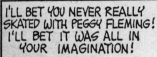

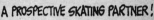

HE'S A GOOD SKATER, BUT HE'S THE FUNNIEST LOOKING KID I'VE EVER SEEN!

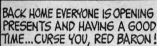

HERE'S THE WORLD WAR I FLYING ACE BACK AT THE AERODROME IN FRANCE..

HE IS SITTING IN THE OFFICERS' CLUB DRINKING ROOT BEER... IT IS CHRISTMAS DAY, BUT HE IS VERY BITTER...

WILL THIS STUPID WAR NEVER END? MUST I GO ON FLYING THESE MISSIONS FOREVER? I'M TIRED OF THIS WAR!

BESIDES, SANTY DIDN'T BRING ME ANYTHING..

YOU'RE IN THE SHADOW OF YOUR OWN GOAL POSTS... YOU ARE A MISCUE... YOU ARE THREE PUTTS ON THE EIGHTEENTH GREEN... YOU ARE A SEVEN-TEN SPLIT IN THE TENTH FRAME... A LOVE SET!

YOU HAVE DROPPED A ROD AND REEL IN THE LAKE OF LIFE... YOU ARE A MISSED FREE THROW, A SHANKED NINE IRON AND A CALLED THIRD STRIKE!

DO YOU UNDERSTAND? HAVE I MADE MYSELF CLEAR?

THE DOCTOR IS IN

PSYCHIATRIC HELP 5¢

THE DOCTOR IS IN

JUST WAIT 'TIL NEXT YEAR!

SCHULZ

THE PEANUTS GALLERY

YOU'RE MY HERO, CHARLIE BROWN   **T2197**
   (selected cartoons from *Peanuts Every
   Sunday,* Vol. 2)

HERE COMES SNOOPY   **T2203**
   (selected cartoons from *Snoopy,*
   Vol. 1)

ALL THIS AND SNOOPY, TOO   **T2204**
   (selected cartoons from *You Can't
   Win, Charlie Brown,* Vol. 1)

FUN WITH PEANUTS   **T2201**
   (selected cartoons from *Good Ol'
   Charlie Brown,* Vol. 1)

HAVE IT YOUR WAY, CHARLIE BROWN!   **T2232**
   (selected cartoons from *Sunday's
   Fun Day, Charlie Brown,* Vol. 2)

75¢ Wherever Paperbacks Are Sold

FAWCETT CREST BOOKS

If your bookdealer is sold out, send cover price plus 15¢ each for
postage and handling to Mail Order Department, Fawcett Publications, Inc., P.O. Box 1014, Greenwich, Connecticut 06830. Please
order by number and title. Catalog available on request.